astronauts

DATE DUE

GAYLORD			PRINTED IN U.S.A.

Lewis TRONDHEIM • Manu LARCENET

NANTIER · BEALL · MINOUSTCHINE
Publishing inc.
new york

ISBN 1-56163-407-7
© Dargaud 2000, 2001 by Tron   and Larcenet
© 2002, 2003 NBM for the Eng   ion
Translation by Joe Johnson
Lettering by Ortho
Printed in China

3   2   1

Library of Congress Cataloging-in-Publication Data

Trondheim, Lewis.
    [Cosmonautes du futur. English]
    [Astronauts of the future / Lewis Trondheim, Manu Larcenet.
      p. cm.
    ISBN 1-56163-407-7 (pbk. : alk. paper)
      I. Larcenet, Manu. II. Title.

PN6747.T76C6713 2004
741.5'944--dc22

2004049960

BOOM, BOOM, BOOM...I WIN SO YOU OWE ME A DIME.

HEY, YOU GOT SOME SORTA TRICK FOR ALWAYS WINNING CHECKERS? HOWYA DOING IT?

CAN'T TELL YOU.

OR...GIMME A DIME AND I'LL TELL YOU HOW.

THAT'S COOL!

SO, WHAT IS IT? WHAT IS IT?

YOU'RE NOT A REAL KID, YOU'RE A ROBOT LIKE EVERYBODY ELSE HERE. YOU ALWAYS PLAY THE SAME WAY, WITH NO IMAGINATION SO IT'S EASY TO WIN.

IT AIN'T SO. I AIN'T NO ROBOT.

YEAH YOU ARE AND I'LL PROVE IT TO YOU!

NO, IT AIN'T SO! YOU'RE THE ROBOT!!

GIMME A DIME AND I'LL SHOW YOU.

HERE...SO WHAT'S YOUR PROOF?

GIMME YOUR HAND....YOU'VE GOT LOTS OF EXTERNAL SENSORS THERE.

YOWIE!

AND IF I PINCH YOU, THEY'LL MAKE YOU PRETEND TO HOLLER SO IT'LL LOOK LIKE YOU'RE HUMAN.

YOU GET HURT, KID?

NO, SIR. I'M A ROBO-DOT.

...NOW THAT YOU ALL KNOW ABOUT HOW CORPORAL BONAPARTE BECAME NAPOLÉON, THINK ABOUT IT AND TELL ME WHAT YOU THINK OF HIM AND HIS STORY.

MATT!

HE....UHH...HE DRESSED FUNNY, I BET HE'D BE EMBARRASSED TO SHOW HIS FACE NOW.

NO, TELL ME SOMETHING MORE PERTINENT.

BOB?

UH...HE DIDN'T HAVE A TOILET SO HE'D POTTY BEHIND THE CURTAINS IN VERSAILLES, BUT AT THE END OF HIS LIFE, WHEN HE WAS ON EASTER ISLAND OR ON THE ISLE OF RÉ, HE MUST'VE BEEN HAPPY...

...'CAUSE THERE WERE BEACH CABINS AND HE COULD USE THE TOILET THERE.

FASCINATING.

NOK NOK

AH, IT'S THE GUIDANCE COUNSELOR.

MISTER PEBBLE, THIS IS A GILBERT HALIBUT, HE'S JUST MOVED HERE.

YES, HE'S ON MY ROLL.

BIG BUTT!

FAT BUTT!

HALF-BUTT!

PFFF!

BUTT-HEAD!

I'LL LEAVE HIM WITH YOU.

AND EVERY-ONE BE NICE TO HIM.

OKAY, TAKE A SEAT BESIDE MARTINA WHO IS ALSO, ONCE AGAIN, GOING TO SHARE WITH US HER DEEPEST THOUGHTS.

HE'S A LITTLE FAT GUY WHO DOESN'T DESERVE ALL THE ATTENTION HE GETS.

YOU KNOW HOW TO PLAY CHECKERS? LET'S PLAY FOR A DIME.

I DON'T TALK TO GIRLS.

I'M NOT A GIRL, I'M A YOUNG LADY.

IT'S NO DIFFERENT, YOU AIN'T GOT A WEE-WEE.

WHATTA YOU KNOW ABOUT IT?!

EVERYBODY KNOWS GIRLS DON'T HAVE WEE-WEES.

YOU GOT PROOF?

I DON'T CARE...ANYWAYS, YOU AIN'T EVEN A REAL KID, YOU'RE AN ALIEN.

AND YOU KNOW WHAT YOU ARE? YOU'RE A ROBOT! A MACHINE!

IT'S TRUE.

I'M A WAR MACHINE... AN ASTRONAUT TRAINED LIKE AN ANIMAL TO CONQUER THE WORST SPACE CREATURES LIKE YOU.

AND THE ASTRONAUT'S SCARED TO PLAY CHECKERS FOR A DIME?

I'M A FEROCIOUS WARRIOR. I DON'T PLAY FOR LESS THAN FIFTY CENTS.

DINNERTIME, MARTINA.

COMING.

IT AFF-LICTS US LIKE A DISEASE ♪

WHERE'S JERRY?

A MEETING RUNNING LATE... HE'LL BE HERE IN AN HOUR.

IT'S JUST A RECIPE FOR HATE.

WHEN YOU WERE LITTLE, DID YOU EVER THINK YOUR PARENTS WERE ROBOTS AND THAT YOU WERE THE ONLY REAL PERSON?

NO, BUT I THOUGHT MY PARENTS WEREN'T MY REAL ONES AND THAT I WAS A PRINCESS ABANDONED WHEN I WAS A BABY.

WAS IT TRUE?

OF COURSE! BUT I PREFERRED MY LIFE HERE.

THE SPLENDORS OF THE COURT, THE GREAT BALLS, AND ALL THOSE ENORMOUS EVENING GOWNS WOULD HAVE BEEN TOO EXHAUSTING FOR ME.

HARDEE HAR HAR! VERY FUNNY!

MARTINA, WE BOTH KNOW THAT THE WORLD'S NOT A VERY NICE PLACE, BUT IT'S UP TO YOU TO FIND THE GOOD THINGS ABOUT IT RATHER THAN DENYING REALITY.

HMM...

YES...OF COURSE... YES...

YES... YES...

TAKING ORDERS FROM HIS ALIEN BUDDIES RIGHT IN FRONT OF ME... HE'S PRETTY BOLD TO LET ME HAVE SUCH A CHANCE TO REVEAL ALL OF THEM...

ASTRONAUT OF THE FUTURE IN ACTION!!

HEY!! GIVE THAT BACK!!

YES... YES...

YES...

LITTLE BASTARD!

GIMME THAT, YOU LIL' THIEF!

YEAHGLP!

IT WASN'T TO STEAL IT, IT WAS TO LISTEN IN.

AND YOU KNOW WHY I'M NOT AFRAID OF YOU?

'CAUSE IN TWO SECONDS YOU'RE GONNA RUN AWAY SHOUTING,,,

...WITHOUT ME LAYING A FINGER ON YOU.

VRIO

HAH...THAT ALIEN DIDN'T DESERVE ME AS A FOE!

WAIT! HANG AT LEA

HEY! GIL... GONNA TELL ME WHATCHA HEARD ON THE CELL PHONE?

EVERY MAN FOR HIMSELF, GIRL!

BE NICE...DID THEY MENTION ROBOTS OR ALIENS?

DON'T TALK TO ME. I DON'T WANT FOLKS THINKING I WAS BREATHING IN AIR COMING FROM YOUR MOUTH.

TELL ME AND I'LL GIVE YOU THE ANSWERS ON THE QUIZ...

AND F+A+R+T, WHAT DOES THAT ADD UP TO?

IF YOU TELL ME, I TELL YOU ANOTHER SECRET.

I DON'T CARE. I KNOW THOUSANDS MORE SECRETS THAN YOU.

GRRM...IF YOU TELL ME, I'LL GIVE YOU A KISS.

I'M IMMUNIZED AGAINST ALL BIOLOGICAL WEAPONS.

RRIIIIIIIING

AND IF I TELL THE PRINCIPAL THAT YOU STOLE A CELL PHONE?

I'M INDIFFERENT TO EVERY SORT OF FEAR.

GULP!

STAY BACK!!
YOU'LL GET ME
SPOTTED!!!

I COULD EASILY TAKE ADVAN-
TAGE OF THIS SITUATION
IF I WERE A PEST.
THEN AGAIN,
MAYBE I
AM ONE?

COME THIS
WAY...
RIGHT NOW
OR I'LL SCREAM!

TAKE
OFF YOUR
SWEATER.

YOU DIRTY GIRL...YOU'RE WORSE
THAN ALIENS!!
DO WHAT I SAY OR
ELSE. YOU KNOW
WHAT A GIRL'S
CAPABLE OF.

IT'S THE LAST TIME I EVER TALK TO A
GIRL! WHEN I GROW UP, I WON'T GET
MARRIED, I'LL GO THE BAR WITH MY
BUDDIES ALL THE TIME...
...AND
TO
DISNEY
WHENEVER
I WANT.

HEY!
WHAT...
WHAT...
WHAT ARE
YOU DOING?
YOU'RE
CRAZY!

PUT ON THIS SWEATER
AND HAT AND
GRAB MY BAG.
HE WON'T RECOGNIZE
YOU. WE'LL MEET UP AT
THE CORNER PAST THE STORE.

I DIDN'T TELL YOU WHAT I
HEARD AND YOU STILL
WANNA HELP ME?!
AND I'LL EVEN
HAVE TO PUT ON YOUR
SWEATER THAT SMELLS
OF AN IDIOT.

ON THE PHONE, THE GUY
DIDN'T SAY ANYTHING
REVEALING HE WAS
AN ALIEN.
I FIGURED
SO, OTHERW
HE'D HAVE H
YOU KILLED.
THE FUTURE,
HAVE TO BE
CAREFUL A
CLEVERER

HI, MARTINA.

OH...GIL!

I THOUGHT OUR OPERATION WOULD BE DELAYED.

NO, NO, WE CAN GO AHEAD.

I'VE GOT A BACKPACK FOR MY SNACK!

WHAT'S THAT?!

IT'S MY SISTER GALE.

MY PARENTS MADE ME BRING HER.

OH, THAT'S JUST GREAT!

MISTER ASTRONAUT OF THE FUTURE CAN'T COME ON A SUICIDE MISSION TO THWART THE ROBOTS' DIABOLICAL PLANS WITHOUT HIS LITTLE SISTER!!

AND WHO SAYS SHE'S NOT ONE OF THEM?

WELL...SHE'S MY LITTLE SISTER, I'VE WATCHED HER GROW UP.

I'M WAY GOOD WITH A MACHINE GUN!

AND YOU'RE HERE WITH A DOG. YOU SURE IT AIN'T AN ALIEN?

THE ALIENS WOULD NEVER SINK LOW ENOUGH TO EAT DOG FOOD.

...WHATTA WE DO? WE ATTACK PEOPLE AND MAKE 'EM TAKE OFF THEIR HUMAN MASKS?

NO. THAT'S TOO CHANCY. I GOT ANOTHER PLAN.

I'M SURE THERE ARE LOTS OF BUILDINGS THAT ARE ONLY USED TO REPAIR ROBOTS OR TO HOUSE UNDISGUISED ALIENS.

IN WHAT KIND OF BUILDING WOULD WE SEE THAT?

IN PLACES WHERE TRUE HUMAN KIDS LIKE US WOULD NEVER THINK OF GOING.

OH, I SEE WHAT YOU MEAN!

NOK NOK

YES?

CAN I COME IN, MARTINA?

UH, YES, JEROME. COME IN.

HAVE A NICE DAY?

YES.

I WALKED THE DOG.

WHAT DID YOU DO?

OH...

OOD...UH... 'LL LEAVE OU ALONE. E YOU FOR DINNER.

OKAY.

ROBOT!

OOOOOOO, YOU'RE SO PRETTY, LITTLE PRINCESS BLUE...

GIL! TELEPHONE!

IT'S MARTINA. I...I THINK I'VE GOT IT...

OH? YOU FIGURED OUT WHY THE...UH...THE CHOCOLATES SHOWED US HOW TO CONTROL THE...JELLY?

YES...I'LL TELL YOU TOMORROW, IT'S TOO HARD TO EXPLAIN IN STEAK. BUT IT'LL SURELY BE THE END OF THE SPAGHETTI...WE'LL EAT 'EM ALL!

OH YEAH, OK...SO YOU'LL TELL ME TOMOR-ROW.

RIIIIIING

MARTINA KNEW TOO MUCH AND IT'S PUT HER IN DANGER! I GOTTA SAVE HER!

ASTRONAUT OF THE FUTURE TO THE RESCUE!

HEY YOU! YOU'RE STAYING AT SCHOOL!

WHAT ARE YOU UP TO?

BLANG!

LET ME GO!! IT'S A MATTER OF LIFE AND DEATH!

YOU'RE GONNA GO RIGHT BACK TO CLASS OR I'LL TAKE YOU TO SEE THE PRINCIPAL.

NO!! YOU DON'T UNDERSTAND IT'S...

BIP BIP B

HELLO. YES?

YES, OKAY.

I'LL TAKE CARE OF IT.

LATER...

IT'S THE END...

THEY'VE GIVEN US THE MEANS TO PROPEL ROCKETS. LOTS OF 'EM WILL BE BUILT AND USING 'EM FOR SPACE TRANSPORTATON WILL BECOME COMMONPLACE.

THAT WAY, ONE DAY, THE ALIENS OR THE ROBOTS WILL ARRIVE ALL AT ONCE WITH THE HELP OF THE SAME ROCKETS AND, COMING IN UNNOTICED, THEY'LL ZAP US ALL!

WOAH!!

AWFUL, ISN'T IT?!

UH, YEAH...I SAT DOWN ON A ROCK AND IT HURT!

PFFF...HOW CAN YOU FIGHT SUCH ALIEN MACHI-AVELIANISM?

WE'RE SMALL STUFF.

I HAVE A PLAN.

OH...NOW I FEEL REAL CONFIDENT.

LOVE BIRDS! LOVE BIRDS!

PRFF...

ASTRONAUT OF THE FUTURE!

YOU'RE NOT SUPPOSED TO HIT A GIRL.

GIRLS ARE STUPID!

UHH...BUT YOU'RE NOT AS BAD AS THE OTH-ERS...

ALL DONE...I'VE PUT AWAY EVERYTHING THAT WAS IN MY BOXES.

IT'S ABOUT TIME.

UH, HEY... ON WEDNESDAY, COULD I GO TO A MOVIE WITH A BUDDY?

HMM... WHICH BUDDY'S THAT?

UH... GEORGE.

HMM, OF COURSE, SWEETIE.

AND YOU CAN TAKE YOUR SISTER WITH YOU. SHE WAS SO HAPPY THE LAST TIME.

I DON'T WANNA!! THE FILM'S RATED KIDS OLDER THAN FIVE!

BEEP BEEEP

HUH? WAIT A SECOND...

YES? ...ES...

...THERE'S A DOLL-EATING TEDDY BEAR AND...AND...

IT'S FOR YOU.

IT'S MARTINA...I MEAN "GEORGE."

YEAH, WHAT?

I'VE GOT THE TRAIN SCHEDULES. THERE'S ONE LEAVING AT 1:35PM, IS THAT COOL?

WHEN DOES IT ARRIVE?

AN HOUR LATER. WE'LL BE AT THE LAB THAT DISCOVERED HOW TO CONTROL ANTIMATTER.

GOOD...I'LL TAKE MY LASER PISTOL JUST IN CASE.

THEY MADE ME BRING HER WITH ME.

I LOVE MOVIES!

IF SHE WANTS TO, BUT IT'S AT HER OWN RISK.

MOMMY GAVE ME SOME RISKS SO I COULD BUY MY TICKET ALL BY MYSELF!

IS THAT THE THEATER?

NO, IT'S A BARN.

IS THAT IT?

NO, THAT'S A BARN.

WHEN WE GET TO THE LAB, WHAT'LL WE DO?

OVER THERE?

DON'T WORRY...WE'LL DO IT LIKE PROS.

OH! COOL!

WE SNIFF IT OUT, GET A BEAD ON THE PLACE, WE IMPROVISE AND ATTACK?

OVER THERE?

NO...

WE ACT LIKE WE WERE ASSIGNED TO DO A REPORT FOR SCHOOL...AND IF THEY DON'T LET US SEE ANY ONE...

WE ATTACK

NO! WE CRY!

HMM... THERE'S NOTHING ON MY SCHEDULE.

THE PRINCIPAL CALLED...IT'S FOR AN ARTICLE IN OUR SCHOOL NEWSPAPER...AND WE TRAVELED 50 MILES JUST TO COME HERE...

WAIT A SECOND, KIDS.

MM!

HUSH!

HERE'S AN ASSISTANT ENGINEER WHO'LL ATTEND TO YOU...

THANK YOU.

HELLO.

MATERALT

MARK PICARD.

MARTINA VALAY.

YOU STAY OUT HERE WITH THE LETTER WE STUCK IN YOUR BACKPACK!

NO!

I WANNA SEE THE MOVIE, TOO!!

WE'RE NOT GOING TO THE MOVIE JUST YET...WE...WE'RE JUST GOING TO SEE IF THERE'S POPCORN AND POPSICLES...IF NOT, WE'LL GO TO ANOTHER THEATER, OKAY?

UH...WOULD YOU TELL ME WHY YOU'RE PINCHING MY HAND?

OH...

AN OLD HABIT, I'M SORRY...

IT'S COOL...MY LITTLE SIS- TER'LL STAY HERE, WE CAN VISIT EVERY- THING...

HE'S NOT A ROBOT, I TESTED HIM.

YOU'RE NOT AUTHORIZED TO VISIT OUR FACILITIES. BUT, YOU CAN HAVE TEN MINUTES TO ASK ME QUESTIONS.

OH...

IN THAT CASE, CAN WE SPEAK IN PRIVATE?

COME IN HERE.

I'M LIS- TENING.

SO...FIRST QUESTION AS A MATTER OF FORM: WHO DISCOVERED HOW TO CONTROL ANTIMATTER?

ARE YOU ON THE ALIENS' PAYROLL OR HAVE THEY FOOLED YOU, TOO?

H...WE'RE NOT ON EARTH?!

THAT MEANS THAT...THE ROBOTS WERE BUILT BY WHOM?

IT'S TOO SOON TO TELL YOU THAT.

IT'S TOO LATE NOT TO TELL US!!

SHE'S RIGHT. THE MAWISSIANS BUILT THE ROBOTS.

WHEN YOU CRASHED, YOU WERE BASICALLY JUST BITS AND PIECES...THEY SAVED YOUR DNA, YOUR MEMORIES, AND CERTAIN BITS OF YOUR BRAINS TO RECONSTRUCT YOU.

GULP!! WE...WE'RE ROBOTS!!

NO...CALM DOWN...IT'S MORE LIKE YOU'RE A SORT OF CLONE.

GULP! CLONES!

MORE THAN CLONES SINCE THERE ARE REAL BITS OF BRAIN AND SINCE THE MAWISSIANS RECONSTRUCTED SCENES FROM YOUR REAL CHILDHOOD...THAT WAY, YOU COULD RELIVE THE SAME THINGS AND BECOME EXACTLY THE SAME AGAIN.

THE MAWISSIANS PLACE A VERY HIGH VALUE ON LIFE AND THE INDIVIDUAL. THEY WERE SO SAD TO SEE YOU IN SUCH A CONDITION.

MY GOD! IT'S WORSE AND WORSE!! AND...AND THE MAWISSIANS? WHERE ARE THEY?

THEY'RE HIDING. THEY'RE AFRAID OF SCARING YOU.

CAN WE SEE THEM!!

HERE'S A HOLOGRAPHIC PROJECTION.

WEREN'T THEY MORE AFRAID THAT WE'D MAKE FUN OF THEM?

ALIENS!! KNEW IT!! I AS RIGHT!!

STOP GLOATING, GIL...

THE WORST IS YET TO COME.

THE WORST? WHAT IS THERE STILL?

OUR MAMAS.

YES...WE'RE THE EXACT REPLICAS OF YOUR MAMAS AND HAVE THE SAME LOVE FOR YOU...

...BUT WE ARE ROBOTS.

NO! IT'S NOT TRUE!

BUT SINCE WE RAISED YOU, WE REALLY ARE YOUR MAMAS THEN...

YOU OKAY, GIL?

UHH...I'M DEALING WITH IT...YUP...

SO...LET ME SUM IT UP: WE'RE NOT ON EARTH, EVERYTHING AROUND US IS AN ILLUSION, THERE ARE ROBOTS EVERYWHERE, ROBOTS THEMSELVES BUILT BY LITTLE ALIENS, WE'RE PRACTICALLY CLONES, AND YOU'RE NOT OUR ORIGINAL MAMAS, INSTEAD WE'RE ADOPTED.

I DON'T THINK IT COULD BE MORE LOGICAL.

SURE YOU HAVEN'T FORGET ANY THING?! IN THE MEANTIME, HA THE EARTH BEEN DESTROYED? HAS A VIRUS EXTERMINATED T HUMAN RACE? OR HAS THE FORMULA FOR MAK-ING CHOCOLATE BEEN LOST?

NO, NO, EVERYTHING FINE.

GOOD...I SUPPOSE I'LL HAVE TROUBLE GET-TING USED TO IT, BUT I'LL BE FINE IN TWO HUNDRED YEARS.

HMM...

THEY HAVEN'T TOLD US EVERYTHING, LOOK...

WHAT?

WHO'S THAT? IT SURE AIN'T OUR PARENTS...

THEY VAGUELY RESEMBLE SOMEONE...

UH... OH YEAH! IT'S FUNNY, IT'S ALMOST LIKE...

NOOOOOOOO!!

LET'S GO BACK TO THE APART-MENT.

THE LAST BLOW WAS THE HARDEST...

CAN GIL AND I BE ALONE?

SURE!

SO? YOU GOT A PLAN SO EVERYTHING CAN BE LIKE IT WAS BEFORE?

LIKE BEFORE WHAT? LIKE WHEN WE WERE ALL SMASHED UP IN OUR CRASHED SPACESHIP? WOULD YOU PREFER A HAMMER OR A PICKAX?

COME ON.

LET'S GO OUTSIDE. I NEED SOME FRESH AIR, TOO.

IF I DIDN'T KNOW BETTER, EVERYTHING LOOKS NORMAL.

CAN YOU JUST IMAGINE THE MONEY THEY SPEND ON US? THEY COULD HAVE RAISED US IN A LUXURIOUS CASTLE INSTEAD OF IN THE SUBURBS.

THAT SAID, IF YOU CAN HEAR US, I'D LOVE TO SEE WHAT THIS PLANET'S REAL SKY LOOKS LIKE!!

WOAH...IT'S INCREDIBLE!

YOU SAID IT... THEY HEARD EVERYTHING WE WERE SAYING FROM THE BEGINNING!

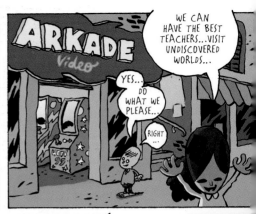

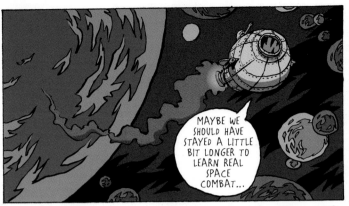

YOU'RE ALSO TOOK "EXTERMINATING STINKING ALIENS"?

YES.

YEAH!!

BUT YOU'RE ROBOTS, HOW WOULD THAT INTEREST YOU?-

LET'S JUST SAY THAT WITH A 3-SECOND DOWNLOAD, WE CAN ABSORB THE INFO ON SEWING AND ELECTRICITY RIGHT UP TO HIGH SCHOOL DIPLOMA LEVEL.

BUT FOR "EXTERMINATION" THERE'S NOT A SINGLE FILE. THERE NOT EVEN AN EXTERMINATION CERTIFICATE!

GOOD MORNING, CHILDREN. I'M PROFESSOR WAHDER. AND THE FIRST ONE WHO GIGGLES WHILE SAYING "PROFESSOR **WATER**" OR "WATER PROF" WILL BE KICKED OUT.

GREAT...

...A ROBOT WITHOUT A SENSE OF HUMOR.

SORRY, YOUNG LADY, I'M PROGRAMMED TO NOT HAVE ANY HUMOR SO YOU CAN HAVE AN ENVIRONMENT WHERE EVERY ROBOT YOU ENCOUNTER IS DIFFERENT.

DON'T GO THINKING THAT ALL ALIENS ARE ALIKE.

YOU HAVE TO BE PREPARED FOR EVERY EVENTUALITY: A FEARFUL ALIEN, A SERIAL KILLER ALIEN, A DRUNK ALIEN, A VACUUM CLEANER SALESMAN ALIEN...

AND WHY ARE YOU HAVING THE CLASS IN A CLASSROOM INSTEAD OF A PLACE WHERE WE CAN TRAIN WITH LASER PISTOLS?

YOU'LL SEE. TAKE OUT YOUR NOTE-BOOKS.

WOW! WE'RE GONNA LEARN HOW TO KILL WITH JUST A NOTE-BOOK?!

NO. YOU MUST UNDERSTAND THE THEORY BEFORE THE APPLICATION.

WE DON'T PUT ATOM BOMBS IN A BABY'S HANDS.

WE'LL START WITH THE THROW-ING OF ROCKS: MASS, VELOCITY, AND IMPACT.

JUST ONE QUESTION: WILL WE GET TO USE LASER PISTOLS OR ATOM BOMBS AFTER-WARDS?

YES.

YESS! WHEN?

AT THE END OF THE SCHOOL CYCLE, MEANING IN ELEVEN YEARS, IF YOU DON'T GET HELD BACK.

NOT VERY WELCOMING.

WHAT DID YOU FIGURE? THEY WEREN'T GOING TO RUIN THEIR BEAUTIFUL PASTURES TO BUILD OUR SUBURB. THEY PLUNKED US RIGHT IN THE MIDDLE OF THE DESERT.

THAT WAY, WE ...'T HAVE TO PUT ... WITH THE FLIES ...M THEIR STU-PID COWS!

LET'S NOT BE LIKE THAT. MAYBE THEY DON'T EVEN HAVE COWS.

YOU'RE RIGHT, THEY SURELY HAVE MUTANT FLIES AND MEGACOWS WITH ROTTEN TENTACLES.

COME ON, LET'S GET BACK, IT'S TOO SCARY OUT HERE. WE'LL END UP THINKING IT'S PRETTY.

POK!

YEAH!!

RIGHT IN THE FAT BELLY OF THE SPACE PIG!!

MODERATE YOUR ENTHUSIASM, GILBERT. THE GOAL FOR THROWING WASN'T TO AIM CORRECTLY.

MARTINA, KNOWING THAT YOU'RE TWO METERS FROM THE TARGET AND THAT USED ABOUT .5 OF A SECOND TO HIT HIM WITH A ROCK OF 215 GRAMS,

AT WHAT SPEED DID YOU SEND THE ROCK AND WOULD YOU HAVE BROKEN A WINDOW THREE CENTIMETERS THICK?

THE SPEED SHOULD BE 2 METERS/0.5 SEC. THAT IS, METERS/SEC...AS FOR THE WINDOW, I DON'T KNOW.

UH...

YOU'D NEED T KNOW T ROCK' DENSIT

EXCELLENT, MARTINA.

YOUR TURN, GILBERT.

TAKE A ROCK AND AIM AT THE FAT SPACE MONSTER.

FOR THE SPEED, YOU DIVIDE THE DISTANCE BY THE TIME.

I DON'T CARE. A DE ALIEN I'D H RIGHT IN T HEAD WOULD ASK ME A QUESTION

IN YOUR HEAD, FAT, ROTTEN ALIEN!!

STOP EVERYTHING! WE HAVE TO SPEAK TO MARTINA AND GILBERT IMMEDI- ATELY.

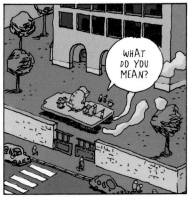

WHAT DO YOU MEAN?

GO SEE YOUR PARENTS OR YOUR FAKE-PARENTS, IF YOU PREFER, AND BID THEM FAREWELL.

FOR A WEEK WE'VE BEEN MONITORING THE APPROACH OF A MESKIMEK VESSEL. WE DIDN'T WANT TO ALARM YOU FOR NO REASON, BUT NOW IT'S CLEAR THAT THEY'RE COMING FOR US.

WHAT ARE MESKIMEKS?

A RACE THAT ABSORBS ALL LIVING BEINGS.

OKAY, WE JUST HAVE TO DEFEND OURSELVES. WHAT SORTA WEAPONS DO YOU HAVE, FAT WAWA?

GREAT WAWA! WE HAVE NO WEAPONS AND EVEN IF WE DID, WE WOULDN'T KILL THE MESKIMEKS TO SAVE OUR OWN LIVES.

BUT...

THERE'S NO ALTERNA-TIVE.

LIFE IS SACRED, BUT IT'S NOT ETER-NAL.

WE'RE GOING TO RETREAT INTO OUR SANCTUARY AND AWAIT DEATH WITH DIGNITY.

FAREWELL, MY YOUNG FRIENDS.

MY STOMACH HURTS.

MY HEAD ACHES.

11

HEY!

WHAT ARE YOU DOING?

I'M TRYING TO DIRECT THIS MACHINE MANUALLY.

THERE! I GOT IT.

IT'S EASIER THAN THE FLIGHT SIMULATORS ON THE PC!

WE'LL START BY GOING TO LOOK FOR MY PARENTS?

NO.

YOURS?

NO.

AND WHAT DO YOU WANT AT SCHOOL? TO GET THE SNACK OUT OF YOUR BACKPACK?

NO.

WE'RE GOING TO GET OUR ONLY CHANCE FOR FIGHTING THE MESKIMEKS.

A ESSENTIAL ADVANTAG IN THE EXTE MINATION ALIENS.

I DON'T UNDERSTAND. NOW YOU WANT TO FIGHT THE MESKIMEKS?

NO! NOT FIGHT THEM, ANNIHILATE THEM.

AND FOR THAT, WE HAVE ONLY ONE WEAPON AT OUR DISPOSAL.

MISTER WAHDER!!

HMMM?

COME QUICK! YOU HAVE TO HELP US BEAT THE MESKIMEKS.

DON'T YOU THINK IT'D BE BETTER TO TAKE ADVANTAGE OF YOUR FINAL MOMENTS?

YEAH...I WILL IN 80 YEARS WHE I'M LOOKIN AT MY PHO ALBUMS! CO ON !

GILBERT! GET MOVING! MARTINA CALLED DADDY AND MOMMY AND WE'RE GONNA PICK THEM UP!

WE'LL MEET UP AT THE TOWN SQUARE IN TWO MIN- UTES.

IF THERE'S STILL A TOWN SQUARE.

17

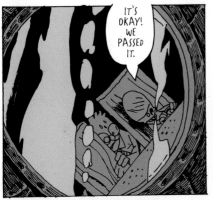

YES!!

KRASH

WOAH!

THEY'RE ALL BLOWING UP ONE AFTER THE OTHER.

DON'T CELE-BRATE TOO FAST.

WHY NOT?! THEY'RE NO LONGER ABLE TO CATCH US.

UH, THAT'S TRUE.

BUT THE EXPLOSION IT CAUSED CAN.

YIKES!

21

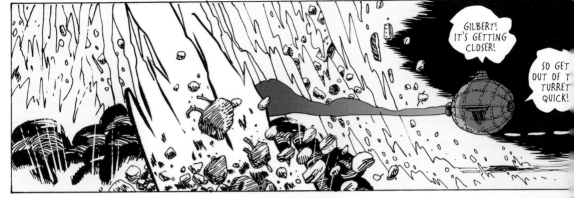

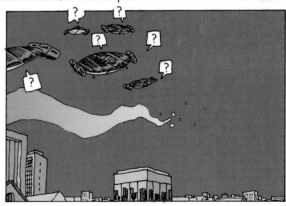

BACK UP!! IT'S A MESKIMEK!!!

YES... AND YOUR SHIP IS STILL IN PIECES.

LOOK.

YOU'VE ALWAYS GRASPED SITUATIONS VERY QUICKLY, CAPTAIN, SO I'LL EXPLAIN EVERYTHING TO YOU BRIEFLY.

I WAS PART OF YOUR CREW WHEN WE CRASHED ON THIS PLANET. AND THE MAWISSIANS BROUGHT ME BACK TO LIFE, TOO, IN A RECREATED MESKIMEK CITY.

GREAT!

IT IS, ISN'T IT? I KNEW YOU'D LIKE THAT.

YES...

CAPTAIN IS A GOOD RANK!

UH, IT'S NOT YOU, GILBERT. MARTINA'S THE CAPTAIN.

HUH?!

YOU'RE SECOND IN COMMAND.

HEY! WAIT!! HOW DO YOU KNOW BETTER THAN I DO?!

IT DIDN'T TAKE LONG FOR MY AMAZING DEDUCTIVE POWERS TO FIGURE OUT THE MAWISSIAN'S PLANS.

DON'T BRAG TOO MUCH, NIKAD. IT WAS REALLY YOUR SMALL TELEPATHIC ABILITIES THAT HELPED YOU UNMASK US.

OKAY, FINE, BUT THE IMPORTANT THING IS THAT OUR TEAM'S FINALLY REUNITED.

OOOOH! LOOK! THERE!

WHERE ARE WE GOING?

MESKURA, MY FAKE CITY OF BIRTH.

I'M JUST GOING TO GET A FEW THINGS.

IN FACT, I HADN'T PLANNED ON CONTACTING YOU TODAY.

BUT, WHEN YOUR SISTER WAS EJECTED, THE CIRCUMSTANCES PROMPTED ME TO INTERVENE RAPIDLY.

YES, I KNOW. YOU WANT TO THANK ME, BUT DON'T KNOW HOW TO DO SO WITHOUT LOSING FACE.

THINK NO MORE ABOUT IT; THANKS ARE ACCEPTED.

I'LL BID MY PARENTS FAREWELL AND I'LL BE RIGHT BACK.

AND STAY HERE, I DON'T KNOW IF MY FAMILY HAS BEEN PROGRAMMED TO NOT EAT YOU.

WE TAKE HIS SHIP AND SCRAM.

HMMM

NO, NO, THIS IS ALL TOO FAST. WE NEED TO TAKE TIME TO REALLY THINK ABOUT IT.

I'M SURE THIS KNOW FEW T

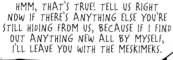

HMM, THAT'S TRUE! TELL US RIGHT NOW IF THERE'S ANYTHING ELSE YOU'RE STILL HIDING FROM US, BECAUSE IF I FIND OUT ANYTHING NEW ALL BY MYSELF, I'LL LEAVE YOU WITH THE MESKIMEKS.

HEY! BE REASONABLE!

DON'T FORGET THAT I'M PROFESSOR WAHDER.

AND THAT YOU OWE ME A MINIMUM OF RESPECT.

AND WITHOUT RESPECT, THERE IS NO CIVILIZATION.

BOMF

AND NOT LOOKING YOUR LISTENERS IN THE EYES, IS THAT RESPECTFUL?

UH... INDEED... I'LL ADD A POINT TO YOUR SEMESTER AVERAGE.

WELL? IS THERE ANYTHING YOU KNOW THAT WE'RE IGNORANT OF?

UH...

NO, NO, NOTHING ELSE.

WELL, YES. JUST THAT A FOURTH PERSON CRASHED AT THE SAME TIME AS YOU.

WHAT?

S, I ALSO READ AT IN HIS MIND, I'VE NEVER SEEN THIS PERSON.

IT'S TIME TO GO LOOKING FOR HIM, AFTER WHICH WE CAN LEAVE THIS PLANET.

AND YOU'LL ABANDON THE MAWISSIANS? YOU'LL LET THEM DIE ALL ALONE HERE?!

WOULD YOU PREFER TO DIE HERE WITH THEM, CAPTAIN?

83

BECAUSE I CAN LET YOU OFF HERE AND IT'LL BE SETTLED QUICKLY. MY FRIENDS HAVE JUST FOUND US AGAIN.

CAN WE CLOAK AGAIN?

NO, NOT RIGHT AWAY, BUT WE CAN ACCELERATE.

OH? AND WILL THAT BE ENOUGH?

WITH THE BOOSTERS, YES.

GOOD! WE SHOULD HAVE JUST ENOUGH TIME TO PICK UP OUR FOURTH TEAM MEMBER.

THERE! THAT'S WHERE HE LIVES. LOOKS UGLY.

COOL!! I'VE ALWAYS WANTED TO VISIT NEW YORK!

GILBERT! IT'S NOT NEW YORK.

I'M PICKING UP TRACES OF A LIVING ORGANISM.

WE'RE CLOSING IN.

THERE, THE APARTMENT IN FRONT.

BE QUICK; THE OTHERS AREN'T FAR BEHIND.

WE'LL DO WHAT WE CAN. BUT, EVEN SO, WHEN WE EXPLAIN EVERYTHING, IT COULD COME AS A SHOCK TO HIM.

ALL THE LIGHTS ARE OUT, HE MUST SURELY BE SLEEPING.

CL7CK

OKAY, LET'S SEE NOW.

HMM, ACCORDING TO MY SCANS, YOU'RE HUMANS.

ACCORDING TO THE SCARE YOU GAVE ME AND ME WANTING TO POP YOU A GOOD ONE IN THE NOSE, I THINK SO, TOO.

YOU'VE GOT TWO SECONDS TO EXPLAIN YOURSELVES, AFTER WHICH I'M GONNA HAVE YOU SHOT.

WE ALL CRASHED ON THIS PLANET MORE THAN THIRTEEN YEARS AGO AND THE MAWISSIANS REGENERATED US AND MADE US RELIVE AN IDENTICAL CHILDHOOD BECAUSE THEY REVERE LIFE ABOVE ALL ELSE.

AND OVER THERE IS A GIANT MESKIMEK VESSEL COMING TO MAKE US ALL INTO HUMAN SAUSAGES. GET IT?

NOT BAD FOR LITTLE SNOT-NOSES.

I SURE WOULD'VE LIKED TO HAVE SEEN WHAT IT'S LIKE TO KILL A REAL HUMAN.

OKAY. I WAS JUST ABOUT TO COMPLETE MY OWN SPACE SHIP, BUT YOURS LOOKS LIKE IT'LL DO.

WHAT ARE YOU WAITING FOR?

I THOUGHT THE EVIL ALIENS WERE COMING.

COME ON. EVERYONE ON BOARD.

I REALLY DON'T LIKE THIS GUY.

YEAH, AND IN TWO MINUTE WE'RE NO DOUBT GON FIND OUT HE'S OUR GENE

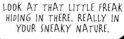

RATHER THAN BATTLING THAT ARMADA, IT'D BE SMARTER TO CHANGE TACTICS.

YOU'RE RIGHT.

HEY!! WHAT ARE YOU DOING?!!

THE CHANGE OF TACTICS WE AGREED ON.

NO REASON TO CRUSH THE WORKER ANTS WHEN YOU CAN GET THE QUEEN.

HUH?!

SURELY YOU'RE NOT GOING TO...

TSK, YOU'RE GETT ON MY NER BABE.

HANG ON!!

HMM, I THOUGHT PILOTING WOULD BE MORE DIFFICULT.

WATCH OUT. WE'RE ARRIVING AT OUR DESTINA- TION.

GILBERT, THAT MISTER MARTH IS COMPLETELY WACKO. WE HAVE TO STOP HIM.

LOOKS LI HE'S FIGUR THINGS O PRETTY G TO ME

SKREEEICH

AND THERE'S THE WELCOME COMMITTEE. I'LL ATTEND TO IT.

TAKE ME TO YOUR LEADER AND...

?

?!

WHAT'S WRONG?

I WANTED TO TAKE CONTROL OF THE MOTHER-SHIP BUT THERE'S A FORCE FIELD AND MY DEVICE ISN'T WORKING.

YOU MEAN IT'S MESSED UP?

SURELY NOT. FIRE AT WILL!!!

HUH?!

BLAM BLAM BLAM BLAM

BJJZZZZ BJJZZZZ BJJZZZZ

THIS GUY'S REALLY BONKERS!!

NOW YOU UNDERSTAND WHY I'M THE CAPTAIN AND NOT YOU?

YOUR MACHINES ARE OUT OF ORDER. SURRENDER, HUMANOIDS!

NEVER!

OKAY, OKAY! WE SURRENDER!

?!!

AND JUST YOU LOOK WHO'S THERE, AS AGREED!

THE MAWISSIANS!

CHILDREN, WE'RE BOTH SAD FOR THE MESKIMEKS AND HAPPY FOR YOU.

YOU'RE STILL ALIVE AND, WHAT'S MORE, YOU WERE ABLE TO BECOME A TEAM AGAIN, A REAL TEAM.

WOULD YOU LIKE FOR US TO CELEBRATE THAT TOGETHER?

BLAM

BLAM

BLAM BLAM

SLAM SLAM SLAM
CLIC CLIC

I'LL COME BACK AND KILL YOU ALL!

I'LL BE OKAY. AT LEAST, I THINK SO.

WHAT THE HELL'S ALL THIS? ANSWER ME!

UH, THAT MISTER MARTH REALLY WASN'T PART OF YOUR TEAM.

HE WAS A VERY DANGEROUS CRIMINAL AND YOU WERE PURSUING HIM WHEN YOU CRASHED ON MAWIS.

AH! THERE'S YOUR VESSEL THAT'S BEEN REPAIRED.

MARTINA, I'LL BE BACK. I HAVE A MISSION AND A MAN TO FINISH OFF.

WAIT FOR ME, LIEUTENANT. I'M COMING, TOO.

?

NIKAD?

MESKIMEKS HAVE THEIR BRAINS IN THE BELLY AND ALL OF OUR EXTREM-ITIES REGENERATE.

PERFECT. DO YOU KNOW HOW TO UNLOCK THE WEAPONS AND HOW TO PURSUE OUR MISTER MARTH?

AFFIRMATIVE. IT STINKS OF HIS EVIL THOUGHTS EVEN HERE.

AND I'M SURE THAT THERE ARE CERTAIN THINGS ABOUT THESE SHIPS THAT HE'S NOT MASTERED AT ALL.

WE'LL TAKE CARE OF YOU.

WHADER! TREAT THE YOUNG LADY.

SO, THE MESKIMEKS WERE ROBOTS, WEREN'T THEY? THERE WASN'T ANY REAL DANGER.

MISTER MARTH WAS A REAL DANGER.

IF ONLY YOU COULD HAVE FE A TOGETHERNE FROM YOUR VICTORY.

MM...

DID I HURT YOU?

NOT YOU, THEM.

THEY SAY THEY RESPECT LIFE OVER ALL ELSE, BUT THEY'RE JUST COLD, CALCULATING, MANIPULATIVE BEINGS.

OU KNEW THAT MISTER MARTH WAS ABOUT TO FINISH HIS VESSEL, THAT 'D TAKEN CONTROL OF HIS ROBOTS, THAT HE WAS A PSYCHOPATH AND THAT SOONER OR LATER HE'D TRY TO KILL YOU ALL.

I BET THAT MISTER WAHDER IS LESS THAN 13 YEARS OLD AND THAT YOU MANIPULAT-ED HIM SO THAT HE'D KNOW AS LITTLE AS POSSIBLE.

I BET THAT YOU SET UP THIS HUGE CHARADE ISO THAT, IN THE END, WE'D KILL THAT MISTER MARTH AND YOU WOULDN'T DIRTY YOUR HANDS AND KEEP A CLEAN CONSCIENCE.

AND THAT YOU WERE SO AFRAID OF HIM THAT I'M SURE YOU'RE HOLOGRAMS.

WHATEVER THE CASE, IT'S ALL OVER.

I WOULDN'T LIKE TO BE WHERE YOUR BRAINS ARE. IT MUSTN'T SMELL TOO GOOD IN THERE!!

IT GOT A LITTLE COMPLICATED, BUT WE ENDED UP GETTING HIM. AND GILBERT'S FEELING A LITTLE SICK TO HIS STOMACH.

FROM THE SHIP'S SHAKING?

NO, FROM REALIZING THAT'D WE'D KILLED A HUMAN BEING.

DON'T WORRY, YOU'RE NOT THE ONE WHO KILLED HIM. I'LL EXPLAIN EVERYTHING.

45

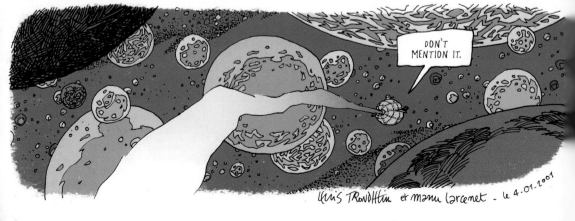